JPIC Gibbon
Gibbons
Mom W9-AJP-366 hero

$16.99
ocn937546317

Mom Told Me You Are A Hero

by
Constance Gibbons

Paula Ottenbreit, Illustrator

Family, friends and community will be enlightened by dialogue bridging generations about trauma induced anger, rage, lost memory, unexpected mood change (PTSD), and injury that can happen within families of veterans. It does not matter if the warrior recently returned or if their war is decades behind them.

vet.er.an: *noun,* old; *adjective,* of long experience; a. a current or former member of the armed forces. b. person of long experience

war.rior: *noun,* a man or woman who is fearless, strong and skilled in great vigor and courage

Text and illustrations copyright @ 2015 by Constance Gibbons

Village Books Publishing
1200 Eleventh Street
Bellingham, WA 98223

Library of Congress: 2015906445
ISBN 978-0-9963198-0-5

Author contact: cogconnexion@gmail.com

We have a veteran in our family. Maybe you do, too. Veterans are also called warriors or heroes.

Your neighbor could be a warrior. A friend of your family, an aunt, or even a teacher at school could be a warrior. A veteran might be a grandparent, like my veteran. A warrior can be a mom, dad, brother or sister, or your uncle. Any grownup you see could be a veteran. Veterans have jobs in places where you shop, or eat, or play, or swim.

Love and honor are reasons women and men go to war.

Veterans care very much about freedom and fairness and the families they love. The strong feeling they have for their country is one reason they decide to serve.

Honor means working hard and doing things the right way.

Honor is easy to remember, like the best homemade ice cream you ever ate! It makes you feel really, really good inside to do things right!

Going to war means change for friends and family left behind.

Families miss veterans when they have to leave home, which makes

everybody sad, but it also makes them stronger.

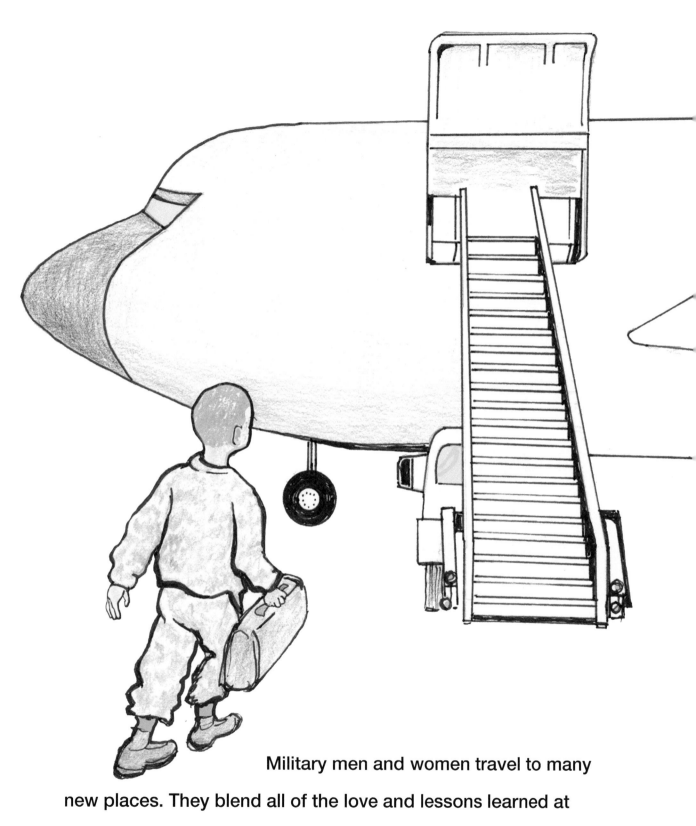

Military men and women travel to many new places. They blend all of the love and lessons learned at home with new skills to become a warrior working at a new job.

Not all people feel grateful for those who go away to war. Just like mean bullies at school who can't seem to keep bad words from tumbling out of their mouths, sometimes adults say unkind things to a veteran. Those words can cause hurt feelings.

Some people believe going to war is wrong. They might wave banners about peace and love.

Veterans want peace too. They fight for our freedom, even for the freedom of those people who say they do not like war. Sometimes people shout unpleasant words to warriors. This can hurt their feelings. I have seen my veteran get sad about this. He worked so hard fighting for his country, even for those who do not believe war is right.

Veterans come in all sizes. They are short or tall, roly-poly round or string bean long and skinny, with hair and skin of red, black, brown, yellow, or white.

Maybe your veteran has no hair, or crazy-wacky hair, or a long gray ponytail and beard.

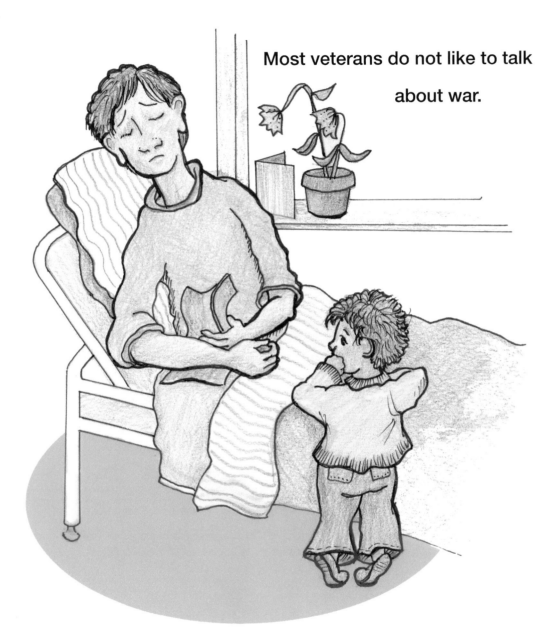

Most veterans do not like to talk about war.

Some hide their feelings deep inside a place you can't see. It is a lot like forgetting something you have hidden deep in your pocket. When you find it again, you remember things about where it came from. If it's something bad, like a bug you could scare someone with, it might frighten you or make you feel upset.

War can change veterans inside and out. Many veterans look or feel different after being at war. They can look tired and seem very sad. Maybe they got hurt during battle or are still in the hospital healing.

It might be the same way for you. Things that can happen to you become part of who you are now and the kind of person you will be later. If you happen to crash your bike and get hurt, you heal but you remember. You might also feel sad and worried, but that experience lets you know to watch out for bumps next time.

Some warriors return from battle with wounds you can easily see which makes them look different. Your veteran might have patches on their skin or squiggly lines, known as scars. New skin could be shiny pink from burns. For certain injuries, your veteran might wear shiny silver or black Transformer-like legs or arms. Their new limbs sometimes match their skin color or have fancy designs on them. They even can have matching bare feet with toenails too!

Sometimes veterans cannot see or hear like they did before.

Burns and other injuries heal to make brand new faces and arms
and legs that keep on loving you and working hard, with the same
big heart on the inside.

Veterans might be remembering places where they have been or friends who have died or been badly hurt from war.

That can make them feel sad or quiet. If your veteran's voice gets really loud, you might think you have made your warrior angry.

When you hurt on the inside the injury can take longer to find and fix. The feelings veterans hide can find their way deep inside.

If there are unexpected loud noises, like firecrackers, they may cause your veteran to stop, stand still and look around. This is a lot like when you have a bad dream and wake up suddenly feeling scared or jumpy. Your veteran's battle memories can cause those feelings too.

I want to tell you something important. When your veteran acts that way, none of it is because of you. Though it might take some practice to not feel bad yourself.

Mom told me my veteran is a hero. But this is what my veteran said to me: "Your mom says that because she is awfully proud of me. The real heroes are those who do not return from battle. They have died for freedom so the rest of us can come home. They have paid the highest cost of war. Those are the true heroes. No, I am not a hero."

I still think my veteran is a hero,

even though he didn't die. He was

brave when it was hard to be brave.

Mom tells me it is my happy spirit that makes everybody, even my veteran, feel better.

I think it is almost magical to be able to change bad feelings into good thoughts and happy memories. First, you can start with little smiles that make your face happy. Then, sit quietly next to your warrior or share a story you each like. Talk softly with your veteran.

Tell a secret. Play a game together. Ask questions and listen to answers. Lie on the grass together and look at clouds. Laugh. Be silly. Be gentle. Be kind. Just be YOU! That's how the bad and sad feelings are chased away for you.

There are many other things that make your veteran especially happy. Veterans are happy through and through when they thank other veterans at parades or ceremonies and while visiting other warriors who are in the hospital healing. It makes all veterans oh-so-proud when you wave your flag at parades and they see your hands held over your heart. That is honor and patriotism.

A grown-up kindness comes from telling a veteran, THANK YOU!

Love is the reason warriors serve their country. And it is exactly

why they want to come home again.

Love them! Your veteran loves you very much, just like mine loves me. You can see it by the twinkle in their eyes.

Mom is right. My veteran is my hero!

CPSIA information can be obtained
at www.ICGtesting.com
Printed in the USA
LVIC06n1504240816
501676LV00020B/271